LFA Health A

C000180413

T'ai Chi Da

Movements 1 – 18

Explained in an easy to follow format

By Sheila Dickinson
President of the LFA Health Arts

Benefits:-
Helps to improve balance and co-ordination
Helps to improve joint mobility
Eases stress
Provides relaxation
Helps to increase your energy

Printed and published in Great Britain by

STAIRWAY
DISTRIBUTION
LTD.

P 0 BOX 19,
HEDON,
HULL
HU12 8YR

First Published 2001

Published by Stairway Distribution Limited
PO Box 19, Hedon. Hull. HU12 8YR
www.leefamilyarts.com

Please consult your Doctor before taking part in the following exercise programme.
The LFA and Stairway Distribution Ltd disclaim any liability for loss or injury in connection with the advice and exercises included in this book.

Acknowledgements

To the past Masters of our Arts - we offer our sincere thanks!

Books by the same author:-

T'AI CHI FORM	(MOVEMENTS 1 TO 140)
T'AI CHI DANCE	(MOVEMENTS 1 TO 184)
T'AI CHI STICK	(MOVEMENTS 1 TO 150)
T'AI CHI SILK	(MOVEMENTS 1 TO 156)
T'AI CHI SWORD	(MOVEMENTS 1 TO 108)
T'AI CHI NUNCHAKU	(MOVEMENTS 1 TO 150)
T'AI CHI FAN	(MOVEMENTS 1 TO 150)

VIDEOS by the same author:-

T'AI CHI FORM	(MOVEMENTS 1 TO 50)
T'AI CHI DANCE	(MOVEMENTS 1 TO 50)
T'AI CHI STICK	(MOVEMENTS 1 TO 50)
T'AI CHI SILK	(MOVEMENTS 1 TO 50)
T'AI CHI SWORD	(MOVEMENTS 1 TO 50)

Available from: -

Stairway Distribution Limited
P O Box 19
Hedon
Hull
HU12 8YR
Tel / Fax 01482 896063

Or visit our Website www.leefamilyarts.com

THE LFA T'AI CHI LIBRARY

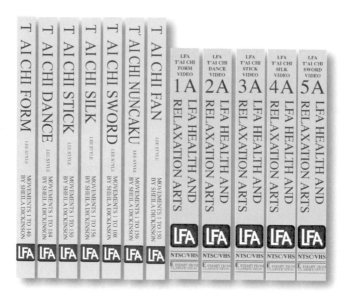

All the above Books and Videos are available from:-

Stairway Distribution Limited
PO Box 19
Hedon
Hull
HU12 8YR
Tel/Fax 01482 896063

You may also order from our Website catalogue, please visit
www.leefamilyarts.com

CONTENTS

Foreword

Welcome to the Lee Family Arts T'ai Chi Dance Set. Please note, I have used the same foreword in each of my books in order that I can pay tribute to my late Grand Master, Chee Soo.

My position as President of the Lee Family Arts started in January 1995. Since that time, I have had the privilege to guide my fellow instructors in all aspects of LFA T'ai Chi, and I have worked hard to reach as many people as possible, so that everyone may gain from the many health benefits of our Arts. I would not be writing this book today without the guidance and patience of my late Grand Master Chee Soo, who spent most of his life teaching the Lee Family Arts. Chee Soo is in my thoughts constantly and I offer my sincere thanks for receiving the benefit of his wisdom and understanding.

Chee Soo wrote five books published by the Aquarian Press, sadly at the time of writing only one title remains in print today 'The Chinese Art of T'ai Chi Ch'uan'. In this book he traces the history of the Lee Style back to Ho-Hsieh Lee circa 1,000BC. It is stated that the Lee Family have always been Taoists and that the Lee Style is a Yin and Yang style, this means that everything within it is in complete balance

1

and harmony. Chee Soo occasionally spoke of his own Grand Master, Chan Kam Lee and told of how they had met during 1934 in Hyde Park in London. In those days there were very few Oriental people in London and the two became friends. It was a friendship that would change Chee Soo's life forever. After Chan Kam Lee's death, Chee Soo dedicated himself to maintaining the knowledge and wisdom he had learnt from Chan Kam Lee.

While staying with my family and myself, Chee Soo talked to me about the future of the Lee Family Arts and the direction he wished them to take.

On Monday the 16th May 1994 Chee Soo asked me to give him my word that I would not let the Lee Family Arts die.

Sadly Chee Soo died on the 29th August 1994.

It is with the greatest respect to Chee Soo that I offer my own writings and understanding of the lessons he taught me.

The names of Instructors who have trained, qualified and still maintain their own training can be obtained from the Lee Family Arts official register of qualified instructors. The LFA can only vouch for the quality and content of that which is taught within an official LFA registered class.

The Lee Family Arts have been tried and tested for thousands of years before we were born. The people who teach them are merely caretakers, who have the privilege of maintaining the Arts, and witnessing them helping others.

This book teaches you all one hundred and eighty four movements of the T'ai Chi Dance. The Lee Family Arts will always be known as a Family Art and it is a family that grows in numbers daily. In concluding, I would like to say a very special welcome to you!

The Tao

What is the Tao? This is a very easy question to answer, at the same time it is a very difficult question to answer. For the Tao is everything and at the same time the Tao is nothing.

The Tao is nothing within nothing, although at the same time it is in all things both inside and out. It is the energy within all things, including us. It is the strength and weakness of every element. We accept that day follows night, spring follows winter, this is simply the natural order of things. In accepting this concept one is automatically accepting the natural order of nature and the way of the Tao. It is sensible to learn to follow the Tao, yet there is no map in the normal sense of the word. The journey which takes each of us a life time to complete, is merely a staging post along the way. Many people spend hours of their time analyzing every detail of their lives, and in doing so they take themselves out of the normal flow of the Tao. My late Master used to say "Sit back and watch the Tao at work". I have to say this is easier said than done, especially when events differ from your own train of thoughts. It takes many years of practise, to understand the wisdom of Chee Soo's words.

We find it easy to look at others and find fault, yet we need to look more closely at ourselves. All too often we upset others without even trying, or do we? The Tao is the strength and weakness of all situations, it is the good and the bad, though neither really exist. People chase Utopia yet does it really exist? It is only the now and how you respond within the now, for the now is everything and the now is nothing. It is the happiness and sadness that dominate our emotions. It is the way of every single individual, of every plant, tree and animal. It is also the clouds that move across the sky, the rain that falls, and the sun that shines. Everyone can find the Tao within themselves, it requires an open mind and one that does not allow analysis to invade the brain.

Within our arts we have special exercises designed to help you on your journey.

Try not to judge things as good or bad, look for the Yin and Yang in all situations. In so doing you will begin to understand the Tao.

We are all born and we will all die, this simple fact applies to all, rich or poor. You do not hear the Tao boast of its work yet if we open our eyes to really see, we can witness the beauty that surrounds us.

Very few of us turn our eyes inwards and appreciate what is happening in each second of our lives. Many of us have heard the saying 'What goes around comes around.' When we are hurt, we demand justice. Hours of our time can be wasted with hurt, resentment, even hatred. The only people we hurt are ourselves. There is no such thing as good or bad luck, there just <u>is</u> and the moment is now, live it! Most of us tend to make even simple tasks complicated, we read only words and not the true meaning behind them, for the true Taoist travels a journey, each step equally as important as the last. Like it or not we are all part of the Tao, we are part of the everything, part of the nothing.

Yin and Yang

We have all heard the expression 'There are two sides to every story', Yin and Yang is about opposites; female, male, sad, happy. Yet it is more complex than this, although at the same time it is easier to understand. Yin cannot exist without Yang or the other way around, yet nothing is completely Yin, within it there is always an element of Yang. At the same time nothing is completely Yang because it contains an element of Yin.

Traditionally Yin represents femininity, body, soul, earth, moon, night, water, darkness, cold, contraction, centripetal motion. Yang represents masculinity, mind, spirit, heaven, sun, day, fire, heat, daylight, expansion, centrifugal motion.

An example of Yin and Yang can be found if we look more closely at the seasons, summer represents Yang, yet it is possible for the rain to fall within summer, representing Yin.

It is also this way with the health of our bodies Yang represents the outer body while Yin represents the inner body. Yet the viscera are Yin and the bowel system is Yang. The right hand side of the body is Yang and the left hand side is Yin. Fruits grown in hot countries (Yang) contain juice (Yin) Vegetables grown in colder countries (Yin) contain more fibre (Yang).

It is a question of balance and harmony, disturbance of the proper balance if left untreated, can in time shorten the life span.

Macrocosmic energy (Li) is Yang and is the natural energy of the universe. Li energy passes through all things every second of the day. In England the strongest period of Li energy is in the summer (Yang) and the lowest in the winter (Yin).

The body's natural internal energy (Chi) is accepted as been Yin. Yet when harnessed with the external energy (Li) they provide the body with a balance of Yin and Yang energies.

The Five Elements

The five elements play an important part in our lives, it does not matter if we understand them or not. If you are experiencing difficulties in your life at the moment, it is because you are out of balance with the five elements. This in turn means you are also out of balance with Yin and Yang, which also means you are out of balance with the Tao. So what are the five elements?

Fire
Wood
Earth
Metal
Water

Each element gives way to the next, for example wood is food for the fire. When it becomes ash it is food for the earth. From the earth comes metal, now metal in its molten liquid form is like water, which is nourishment for the trees, which gives us wood which feeds the fire.

However each element is also capable of destroying the other, for example metal can cut down wood, wood can take the nourishment from the earth, earth can absorb or damn water, fire turns water to vapour.

My late Grandmaster Chee Soo, taught that the organs of the body related to the five elements.

The five Yang organs in the body are as follows:-
Small Intestine (fire)
Gall bladder (wood)
Stomach (earth)
Large Intestine (metal)
Urinary Bladder (water)
The five Yin organs in the body are as follows:-
Heart (fire)
Liver (wood)
Spleen (earth)
Lungs (metal)
Kidneys (water)
The liver, (wood) is in charge of the muscles and tissues.
The heart, (fire) is in charge of the arteries and the texture of the body.
The spleen, (earth) is in charge of the flesh, including the lips.
The lungs, (metal) are in charge of the skin and hair.
The kidneys, (water) are in charge of the bones and nails.
The liver passes energy to the muscles, which help to keep the heart strong. The heart nourishes the blood and arteries, they pass the nourishment onto the spleen, which takes care of the flesh, also giving added strength to the lungs. The lungs feed the skin and hair and also help the kidneys. The kidneys feed the bones and nails and nourish the liver.
If the body's energy levels drop, each organ will draw

from the other, draining the body. In some cases this can be very severe leading to many serious illnesses. Chinese cures are offered within the five elements as follows:-

Acupuncture (metal)
Spiritual Cure (fire)
Chang Ming (wood)
Herbal Therapy (earth)
Thermogenesis (water)

The colours represented by the five elements are as follows:-

Green /Blue (wood)
Red (fire)
Yellow (earth)
White (metal)
Black (water)

This links to the body in the following way, a very red complexion could indicate heart problems. Green/blue tint to the skin may indicate liver problems. Yellow is related to the spleen and pancreas it may also indicate jaundice. Very pale white skin may indicate lung problems. Black/brown may indicate kidney problems. To give your body the best possible nourishment we recommend practising all aspects of the LFA Health Arts which are:-

T'ai Chi Form, Dance,. Stick, Silk, Sword, Nunchaku, Fan, Broad Sword, Umbrella, Knife, Chop Sticks, Taoist Walk, K'ai Men – Chi Kung, Breathing Exercises, Awareness Techniques, Feng Shou (self defence) Chi Shu and Chang Ming (diet).

Taoist Walk

The Taoist walk is an extremely important part of the LFA health training because it moves the weight from one leg to another in a special and subtle way. Not only is one leg working while the other one rests, but the working leg is the Yang leg and the resting leg is the Yin leg.

The weight is moved from one leg to the other before you try and alter the position of your foot.

Start with your feet slightly wider than shoulder width apart, toes pointing forwards. Both hands are held with the palms facing each other.

1/ Drift your weight across to your right side, your right knee bends, your hips and your bottom move across to the right side.

2/ Now take a very small step forwards with your left foot, placing your heel down first. Allow your left knee to bend, move your hips and bottom across to the left. Keep your right leg straight, do not lock your right knee.

Practise walking across the room in this manner. People suffering from back, hip, knee and ankle problems, reap great benefits from practising the Taoist Walk.

We use the Taoist Walk in all of our form sets. With practise it can be incorporated into your every day walk (so that it is undetectable), only you will know the benefits you are receiving each time you place one foot in front of the other.

The Taoist Walk helps to move your Chi energy into the lower part of your body. In the West we tend to carry a lot of congestion around the pelvic area, this stagnation leads to the above mentioned problems. So it is a good idea to learn to walk the Taoist Way. Please try it for yourself, especially if you wake up in the morning feeling stiff, a few minutes practising the Taoist Walk could help to make you feel like a new man or woman.

Etiquette

The etiquette is something that has been handed down through the centuries along with the T'ai Chi, I personally feel it represents a respect for the Arts we are practising and the ancient Masters to whom we owe so much.

When entering or leaving a training hall a student should bow to the room. This bow consists of bending forwards from the waist, at the same time both palms rest on your thighs.

If you arrive after a class has already started you should walk round to the front of the hall, bow to the person taking the class and wait for them to bow to you in return (using the bow explained below).

At the beginning of a class the bow consists of placing your right arm on top of your left in front of your body, your right hand palm faces down down, and your left palm faces up.

When training with a partner you should both bow to each other at the start and finish (using the same bow as when entering and leaving the training room).

If an instructor offers you guidance with your training, you should bow to them after they have finished teaching you, (again using the bow for entering and leaving the training room).

LFA T'ai Chi Dance Set

The LFA T'ai Chi Dance is designed to activate and stimulate the mind. The movements of our T'ai Chi Dance are Yang, this means that they are more flamboyant compared to those of our T'ai Chi Form.

To harness the special breathing techniques used in our Dance, you should breathe in through the nose on the odd numbers and out through the mouth on the even ones.

The breath we use is a Yin breath, this type of breathing uses the upper part of the lungs. Every movement used within all of our sets should be practised without strain. Our Dance is not a dance that is usually practised to music, although it can be. The T'ai Chi Dance has its roots in the five elements and Li energy, including their respective colours. Our T'ai Chi Dance has a beautiful sequence of soft graceful flowing movements.

There are one hundred and eighty four movements in our T'ai Chi Dance and each one is fully explained in this book. I have written this book to help every one enjoy and gain from the many health benefits our Dance has to offer. I personally find the Dance an excellent tonic if I am feeling tired or at a low ebb. I strongly advise against practising our Dance before going to bed. Remember it activates and stimulates, if you attend an LFA T'ai Chi evening class, your instructor will be able to give you the correct exercises to enable you to close down so that you may enjoy a good nights sleep.

LFA T'ai Chi Stances

From the beginning of your training the LFA emphasise the need for good stances. Stances provide your roots, without correct weight distribution and good balance, you will fall over. The body should not be held rigidly, strive for the middle path. To achieve this can take many hours of pleasant practise. My late Master described the body as a tree, the legs are the roots and the arms the branches. Each has its own job to do, while at the same time each is separate, yet each is part of the other. Another example of how Yin and Yang works.

Although you are probably eager to press on and learn the movements of our Dance set. I advise you to take some time to familiarise yourself with the names and the weight distribution of the stances.

From the moment you start to practise LFA T'ai Chi you are beginning to use your Chi energy. <u>In the LFA we teach you how to connect valuable energy points within your own body.</u> The LFA do not promise carrots they cannot deliver. We have specialised breathing techniques to harness the Li energy, it is sometimes known as 'macro-cosmic' energy or the energy of the universe.

Students who attend our day courses become more aware of their own Chi energy, sometimes known as the internal or Yin energy, it is the energy within your own body. Li energy is also known as the Yang energy, it is the external energy. The LFA can teach you how to gain control over both energies to help you to improve the quality of your life. It is a good idea to practise the stances in front of a mirror, if you attend a regular class your instructor will be able to advise you. For those of you unable to attend classes, take the time to make sure you are comfortable with each posture before you move on to the next.

Active Leopard Stance

To achieve a Right Active Leopard stance, stand with your feet slightly wider than shoulder width apart, now drift your weight across to your right side (bending your right knee). Your left leg should be straight with the heel of your left foot lifted off the floor.

To achieve a Left Active Leopard stance, drift your weight across to your left side (knee bent). Your right leg should be straight with the heel raised.

Bear Stance

Bear stance is achieved by standing with your feet shoulder width apart. Your body should be relaxed, without tension. Both of your arms should be hanging loosely by your sides. You should be looking straight ahead.

We use Bear stance at the beginning of all of our sets, when we adopt the 'Prepare' position.

Bee Stance

To achieve Bee stance, place both heels together (toes pointing slightly outwards) and bend both knees. Your arms hang loosely by your sides. You should be looking straight ahead.

Cat Stance

To achieve Right Cat stance, the left leg is bent at the knee, the heel is raised on your right foot. The ball of the right foot rests lightly on the floor with eighty percent of your weight on your left leg.

To achieve Left Cat stance, the right knee is bent at the knee, the heel is raised on your left foot. The ball of the left foot rests lightly on the floor with eighty percent of your weight on your right leg.

Chicken Stance

To achieve Right Chicken stance, turn ninety degrees to your right. Now place most of your weight onto your right leg (bending the knee), Then bend and lower your left knee towards the floor. This is quite a strong stance, it is important that you listen to your own body and do not strain.

To achieve a Left Chicken stance turn ninety degrees to your left, placing most of your weight onto your left leg (bending the knee), then bend and lower your right knee towards the floor.

Crane Stance

To achieve Right Crane stance, take your weight onto your left leg (bending your left knee slightly to aid your balance). At the same time raise your right leg (bending the knee) until your thigh is parallel with the floor. Students who have difficulty balancing should use a right Cat stance.

To achieve a Left Crane stance, simply raise your left leg (bending the knee) until your thigh is parallel to the floor.

Dog Stance

To achieve Right Dog stance, take your weight onto your left leg (bending the knee slightly to aid your balance). At the same time extend and raise your right leg forwards, your leg should be at a height that is comfortable to you without strain.

To achieve a Left Dog stance, simply repeat the above on the opposite side.

Dragon Stance

To achieve Right Dragon stance, step forwards from either a Bear or an Eagle stance. It is important not to over step, make sure you have a good gap width ways between your feet. Drift your weight over to your right side, so that the weight is spread between your right hip, knee and ankle. Eighty percent of your weight should be on your right leg. Your left leg should be straight although not locked.

To achieve a Left Dragon stance follow the same procedure as above this time stepping forwards with your left leg.

Duck Stance

To achieve a Right Duck stance from an Eagle stance, step behind with your left foot, placing your heel down first. Now drift your weight onto your left leg (bending your knee) your right leg should be straight, although not locked.

To achieve a Left Duck stance repeat the above procedure, this time stepping behind with your right foot.

Eagle Stance

Eagle stance is achieved by placing both heels together, toes pointing slightly outwards. Your weight should be evenly balanced between both legs. Your body should be relaxed and without strain.

Flighted Dragon

To achieve a Right Flighted Dragon stance, step through into a Right Dragon stance and then raise the heel of your left foot.

To achieve a Left Flighted Dragon stance, step through into a Left Dragon stance and then raise the heel of your right foot.

Frog Stance

To achieve a Frog stance, stand with your feet slightly wider than shoulder width apart, now bend both knees and lower your weight right down. Remember to listen to your own body, please do not strain.

Leopard Stance

To achieve a Right Leopard stance, take a pace off sideways to your right (bending your right knee and drifting your weight across). At the same time straighten (but do not lock) your left leg.

To achieve a Left Leopard stance, repeat the above procedure stepping off to the left.

Monkey Stance

To achieve a Right Monkey stance, step back with your left foot (bending your left knee). Your right leg is straight with the toes of your right foot raised.

To achieve a Left Monkey stance, repeat the above procedure stepping back with your right.

Riding Horse Stance

To achieve a Riding Horse stance, stand with your feet slightly wider than shoulder width apart (both knees bent) your weight should be evenly distributed between both legs. Your body should be relaxed, without strain.

Scissors Stance

To achieve a Right Scissors stance, drift your weight onto your left leg (bending your knee slightly). Now cross your right leg behind and slightly beyond your left leg, raising the heel of your right foot.

To achieve a Left Scissors stance, repeat the above procedure this time stepping behind with your left foot.

Snake Stance

To achieve a Right Snake stance, take a small pace forwards with your right leg. Both knees are slightly bent, your weight is evenly distributed between both legs.

To achieve a Left Snake stance, repeat the above procedure this time stepping forward with your left leg.

Stork Stance

To achieve a Right Stork stance, take your weight onto your left leg (bending your left knee slightly to aid your balance). Now raise and bend your right leg, taking your foot behind you.

To achieve a Left Stork stance, repeat the above procedure on the opposite side.

List Of Stances 1 - 184

1	Eagle
2	Right Dragon
3	Eagle
4	Left Dragon
5	Left Duck
6	Right Dragon
7	Left Leopard
8	Left Crane/Dog
9	Bee
10	Riding Horse
11	Left Dragon
12	Right Dragon
13	Left Dragon
14	Left Cat
15	Left Crane
16	Left Leopard
17	Left Dragon
18	Left Cat
19	Left Dragon
20	Right Dragon
21	Left Scissors
22	Left Duck
23	Left Dog
24	Left Dragon
25	Left Dragon
26	Right Dragon
27	Left Dragon
28	Left Leopard
29	Right Dragon

30	Right Cat
31	Left Duck
32	Right Duck
33	Left Duck
34	Extended Left Duck
35	Right Cat
36	Left Cat
37	Left Crane
38	Left Dog
39	Right Chicken
40	Left Dragon
41	Right Dragon
42	Right Dragon
43	Left Dragon
44	Left Crane
45	Left Dragon
46	Left Leopard
47	Right Dragon
48	Left Dragon
49	Left Leopard
50	Right Dragon
51	Right Dragon
52	Left Dragon
53	Left Leopard
54	Right Dragon
55	Left Dragon
56	Left Crane
57	Left Dragon
58	Eagle
59	Bee
60	Left Dragon

61	Extended Left Duck
62	Right Crane
63	Left Crane
64	Right Snake
65	Right Duck
66	Right Duck
67	Left Duck
68	Left Duck
69	Right Duck
70	Right Duck
71	Right Dragon
72	Right Monkey
73	Left Leopard
74	Right Dragon
75	Left Dragon
76	Left Cat
77	Right Monkey
78	Right Dragon
79	Right Duck
80	Left Dragon
81	Left Cat
82	Left Dog
83	Right Chicken
84	Left Active Leopard
85	Right Dog
86	Right Dragon
87	Left Cat
88	Left Dog
89	Left Active Leopard
90	Right Dog
91	Right Flighted Dragon

92	Left Dragon
93	Left Crane
94	Left Dragon
95	Eagle
96	Left Leopard
97	Right Dragon
98	Right Cat
99	Right Dog
100	Left Dragon
101	Left Cat
102	Left Dog
103	Left Dragon
104	Frog
105	Left Leopard
106	Right Dog
107	Right Dragon
108	Left Dragon
109	Right Monkey
110	Left Dragon
111	Left Duck
112	Right Dragon
113	Left Stork
114	Left Scissors
115	Bear
116	Left Crane
117	Left Dragon
118	Right Dragon
119	Left Dog
120	Left Dragon
121	Left Dragon
122	Right Dragon

123	Left Dragon
124	Left Dragon
125	Right Dragon
126	Right Monkey
127	Right Dragon
128	Extended Left Duck
129	Extended Left Duck
130	Right Snake
131	Left Crane
132	Left Crane
133	Left Dragon
134	Left Duck
135	Left Cat
136	Left Crane
137	Left Crane
138	Left Dragon
139	Right Dragon
140	Left Dragon
141	Left Leopard
142	Left Stork
143	Left Dragon
144	Right Crane
145	Left Flighted Crane
146	Left Dragon
147	Right Dog
148	Right Dragon
149	Right Crane
150	Riding Horse
151	Riding Horse
152	Left Dragon
153	Left Monkey

154	Right Dragon
155	Left Dragon
156	Left Monkey
157	Right Monkey
158	Left Dragon
159	Right Snake
160	Eagle
161	Right Dog
162	Left Dog
163	Left Scissors
164	Right Monkey
165	Right Dragon
166	Right Monkey
167	Left Cat
168	Left Cat
169	Left Monkey
170	Left Dragon
171	Left Dragon
172	Right Dragon
173	Left Dragon
174	Right Leopard
175	Left Dragon
176	Left Dog
177	Left Cat
178	Right Cat
179	Right Dog
180	Bear
181	Bear
182	Bear
183	Bear
184	Eagle

Prepare

Start in Eagle stance, heels together, toes pointing slightly outwards, both arms hang loosely by your sides. Take a pace out sideways to your left, feet shoulder width apart, placing your heel down first. In LFA T'ai Chi we always place the heel down first. This is because our Arts are based on Chinese Medicine, placing the heel down first ensures the channels open in the correct order.

Number 1

From Prepare, drift your weight slightly onto your right, leg as you draw your left leg into Eagle stance (now centre your weight)

At the same time your right arm circles up to finish with the palm facing away from you. Your fingertips are angled to the left. Your left arm stays by your side but with your palm facing the floor, (you have an energy centre in the centre of the palm of your hand, this should face the floor) see photograph.

Number 2

From Eagle stance turn ninety degrees to your right, into Right Dragon stance. This is achieved by allowing your weight to drift on to your left leg, now pick up your right foot and place it into position (stepping to the right and slightly to the rear, remember to place your heel down first). Drift your weight across to your right leg. Next adjust your left foot by pivoting on the heel, then lower your toes.

Before you turn, circle your right hand to the left and down past your left thigh (you make your turn as your hand reaches your right leg). Your right hand finishes extended forward at shoulder height (fingertips angled to the left). Your left hand does not move.

Number 3

From Right Dragon stance spin two hundred and seventy degrees to your right (so that you are facing the front again) you should now be in Eagle stance (heels together toes pointing slightly outwards). IF YOU ARE UNABLE TO SPIN, MOVE FROM RIGHT DRAGON STANCE BACK TO EAGLE.

At the same time as you spin allow your left arm to come up to shoulder height, finishing with both arms extended sideways (fingertips pointing to the ceiling).

Number 4

From Eagle stance turn ninety degrees to the left into Left Dragon stance. To achieve this drift your weight onto your right leg, pick up your left foot and place it into position, (placing your heel down first), now drift your weight on to your left leg. Adjust your right foot heel and toe.

Before you make your turn circle both arms up and in front of your head until they cross at the wrists (left hand furthest away from you), now lower both arms down the centre line of your body. As you turn to your left, your left arm extends forwards from your left shoulder (fingertips pointing slightly to the right) your right hand is by your side palm facing the floor.

Number 5

From Left Dragon stance drift your weight back onto your right leg (bending your right knee) at the same time straighten your left leg. You are now in Left Duck stance.

At the same time your right hand moves forwards (palm facing up) then over, taking your arm out behind your right shoulder. Your left hand moves down from shoulder height to finish in front of your left thigh (palm facing down) fingertips pointing forwards.

Number 6

From Left Duck stance step forwards with your right leg into Right Dragon stance, this is achieved by drifting your weight first on to your left leg, then onto your right leg after you have stepped forward.

At the same time your right arm extends sideways, level with your shoulder (palm facing down) and then moves underneath your left forearm, (palm turning upwards). The movement continues until the fingertips of your left hand are level with your right wrist.

Number 7

From Right Dragon stance step through with your left foot turning it ninety degrees to the right, transfer your weight onto it (bending your left knee) now straighten your right leg, pivoting on your right heel. Both feet should be pointing straight ahead, you are now in Left Leopard stance.

At the same time as you turn, both arms drift out sideways to shoulder height, fingertips angled slightly forwards. You should be looking at your right hand in this movement.

Number 8

From Left Leopard stance turn ninety degrees to the left into Left Crane/Dog stance, this is achieved by pivoting on the heel of your right foot. Now place your weight onto your right leg, bending your right knee to aid your balance. Raise your left leg, with your knee bent, this movement is in between a Crane and a Dog stance.

At the same time move your right elbow into your waist, your right palm is facing to the left. Your left hand moves up and in front of the left hand side of your head (palm facing away from you, fingertips pointing to the right).

Number 9

From Left Crane stance turn ninety degrees to your right (pivoting on your right heel) into Bee stance. Both heels are together, with your toes pointing slightly outwards, bend both knees.

At the same time your right arm moves forwards to shoulder height (slightly bent with your palm facing in). Your left hand moves down just below your waist (palm facing in).

Number 10

From Bee stance step off with your left foot into Riding Horse stance, feet slightly wider than shoulder width apart, both knees bent.

At the same time your hands change places, your left hand is now in front of your left shoulder and your right hand is just below your navel.

Number 11

From Riding Horse stance drift your weight across onto your right leg, then step forty five degrees (left diagonal) into Left Dragon stance.

At the same time your right hand extends forward (palm facing the centre of your body). Your left hand (palm also facing in) moves to the centre of your body, just below your waist.

Number 12

From Left Dragon stance turn one hundred and eighty degrees to your right into Right Dragon stance. This is achieved by drifting your weight back onto your right leg, then pivoting on the heel of your left foot. Next drift the weight back onto your left leg then pick up your right foot and step into Right Dragon stance,

drifting your weight onto your right leg.

Before you move your legs, sweep both arms up (extended forwards in front of your shoulders) wrists drooped, then turn the hands so that the palms face away from you (fingertips pointing to the ceiling). Now lower both arms as you turn your body, then allow them to sweep up extended in front of your shoulders (palms facing away from you, fingertips pointing to the ceiling).

59

Number 13

From Right Dragon stance turn one hundred and eighty degrees to your left into Left Dragon stance, reversing the leg movements for number twelve.
At the same time form a ball with the left hand on the top.

Number 14

From Left Dragon stance turn forty five degrees to the left into Left Cat stance (right leg slightly bent, the ball of the left foot is resting lightly on the ground).

Still holding your ball shape, your hands move across to the left side of your body (see photograph).

Number 15

From Left Cat stance raise your left leg into Left Crane stance (left knee bent, thigh parallel to the floor).

At the same time both arms sweep across in front of the body, right arm extended outwards at shoulder height (wrist drooped, fingertips pointing downwards). Left hand stops level with your right armpit (wrist drooped, fingertips pointing downwards).

Number 16

From Left Crane stance turn ninety degrees to the right into Left Leopard stance (your left leg is bent, your right leg is straight, both feet pointing straight ahead).

At the same time both hands turn palms facing away from you (on the diagonal) fingertips pointing to the ceiling (see photograph).

Number 17

From Left Leopard stance turn ninety degrees to your left into Left Dragon stance. To achieve this first drift your weight on to your right leg then step into Left Dragon Stance.

At the same time turn your right hand so that your fingertips point to the left and your palm faces towards you. Your left hand remains with the palm facing away from you, fingertips pointing to the ceiling (see photograph).

Number 18

From Left Dragon stance draw back into Left Cat stance (the ball of your left foot is resting lightly on the floor, your right knee is bent).

At the same time circle your arms to the left then in front of your body finishing with your right arm by your side (palm facing the floor). Your left hand finishes palm facing down, level with your right elbow.

Number 19

From Left Cat stance step forward with your left leg into Left Dragon stance drifting your weight across to the left side of your body.

At the same time your right arm moves up and in front of your head (palm facing forward, fingertips pointing to the left). Your left arm moves by your left side (palm facing the floor).

Number 20

From Left Dragon stance step forwards with your right leg into Right Dragon stance. At the same time your left hand moves upwards on the diagonal (palm facing down). Your right arm moves downwards and behind you on the diagonal (palm facing down), you are looking down at your right arm.

Number 21

From Right Dragon stance drift your weight back onto your left leg, now pivot ninety degrees to the right with your right foot. Place your weight on your right leg bending your knee and raise the heel on your left foot. You are now in Left Scissors stance.

At the same time your right arm moves by your side (palm facing down). Your left arm finishes with your hand level with your right elbow (palm facing down) see photograph.

Number 22

From Left Scissors stance turn two hundred and seventy degrees to your left into Left Duck stance (right knee bent, left leg straight).

At the same time your right hand turns palm up and finishes extended behind you at shoulder height. Your left hand finishes palm facing down at waist height.

Number 23

From Left Duck stance raise your left leg into Left Dog stance.

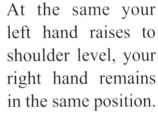

At the same your left hand raises to shoulder level, your right hand remains in the same position.

Number 24

From Left Dog stance lower your left leg and drift your weight forward into Left Dragon stance.

At the same time push your right arm forward at shoulder height (palm facing away from you, fingertips pointing to the ceiling). Your left arm moves by your left side (palm facing the floor).

Number 25

For movement number twenty five stay in Left Dragon stance.

Your left arm remains by your side, but this time turn your left palm up with your fingertips pointing forwards. Your right hand turns palm facing down, see photograph.

Number 26

From Left Dragon stance, step forwards with your right leg into Right Dragon stance.

At the same time your right arm circles over to your right side, finishing with the palm facing the floor. Your left arm finishes extended forward at shoulder height (palm facing away from you, fingertips pointing to the ceiling).

73

Number 27

From Right Dragon stance, step forward into Left Dragon stance.

At the same time your right hand comes to rest inside your left knee (palm facing your knee). Your left palm faces the floor, by your left side.

Number 28

From Left Dragon stance turn ninety degrees to your right into Left Leopard stance (remember to use your Taoist Walk).

At the same time your right hand circles to the right and over, finishing with your palm facing away from you and your fingertips pointing to the left, at shoulder height. Your left hand moves upwards with your elbow bent, palm facing away from you, fingertips pointing to the ceiling (see photograph).

Number 29

From Left Leopard stance turn ninety degrees to your right into Right Dragon stance, this is achieved by picking up your right foot and placing it into position (using the Taoist Walk).

At the same time your left arm moves and extends forwards from your left shoulder (palm facing forwards, fingertips pointing to the ceiling). Your right arm finishes by your right side (palm facing the floor).

Number 30

From Right Dragon stance drift your weight back onto your left leg, bending your left knee. Draw your right foot back flat then raise your right heel, you are now in Right Cat stance.

At the same time turn your right palm up with your fingertips pointing forwards. Your left hand moves across to finish with your wrist drooped, fingertips pointing down near your right armpit.

Number 31

From Right Cat stance step behind with your right foot (heel down first). Drift your weight back onto your right leg and straighten your left leg, you are now in Left Duck stance.

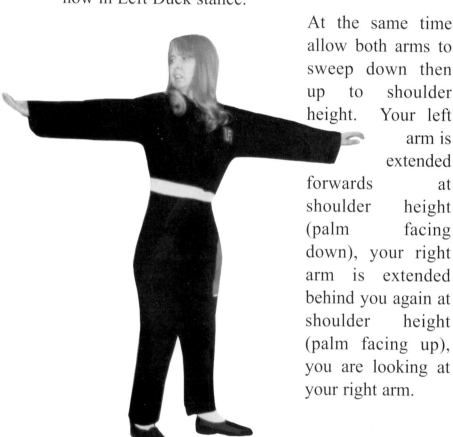

At the same time allow both arms to sweep down then up to shoulder height. Your left arm is extended forwards at shoulder height (palm facing down), your right arm is extended behind you again at shoulder height (palm facing up), you are looking at your right arm.

Number 32

From Left Duck stance step behind with your left foot (heel down first). Transfer your weight onto your left leg and straighten your right leg, you are now in Right Duck stance.

At the same time allow your arms to sweep down then up to shoulder height, (both palms are facing down) you are looking straight ahead.

Number 33

From Right Duck stance step behind with your right foot (heel down first), drift your weight back onto your right leg and straighten your left leg, you are now in Left Duck stance.

At the same time allow both arms to sweep down then up, your left arm is extended forwards in front of your left shoulder (palm facing away from you, fingertips pointing to the ceiling). Your right arm is extended sideways at shoulder height and slightly to the rear (diagonal), your wrist is drooped and your fingertips point downwards.

Number 34

From Left Duck stance step slightly to the rear and deepen your stance, this is Extended Left Duck stance.

At the same time your left hand swoops down to stop in front of your left shin (p a l m facing down), your right arm stays in the same position as it was in for movement thirty three.

Number 35

From Extended Left Duck stance step forward with your right foot into Right Cat stance (the ball of your right foot resting lightly on the floor, your left knee is bent).

At the same time circle both arms around in front of your body (waist height, palms facing in) see photograph.

Number 36

From Right Cat stance place your right heel down and raise your left heel, bending your right knee you are now in Left Cat stance.

At the same time your right arm circles above and in front of the right hand side of your head (palm facing away from you, fingertips pointing to the left). Your left arm is by your left side palm facing down.

Number 37

From Left Cat stance raise your left leg into Left Crane or Left Stork (this turn can be a little difficult, in some cases our students walk round) turn one hundred and eighty degrees to the right.

Your right hand remains in the same position it was in for the last movement. Your left hand extends forwards at shoulder height, palm facing downwards.

Number 38

Turn one hundred and eighty degrees to your right (still in Left Crane or Stork stance) then extend your left leg forwards into Left Dog stance.

Your hands remain in the same position.

Number 39

From Left Dog stance step directly behind with your left foot, placing the ball of your foot on the floor. Bend your right knee as you lower your body down (your left knee should be nearly touching the ground). You are now in Right Chicken stance.

At the same time point the fingertips of your left hand towards the ceiling, your palm faces away from you. Your right arm moves by your side (palm facing the floor).

Number 40

From Right Chicken stance step forwards with your
left leg into Left Dragon stance.

At the same time
your right hand
moves palm facing
in fingertips
pointing to the left
(slightly in front of
your left hand).
Your left arm is
extended forwards
at shoulder height
(palm facing away
from you, fingertips
pointing to the
ceiling).

Number 41

From Left Dragon stance turn one hundred and eighty degrees to your right into Right Dragon stance.

At the same time both hands turn in to face your body (shoulder height) fingertips pointing towards each other.

Number 42

Stay in Right Dragon stance for number forty two. Turn both palms so that they face away from you with your fingertips pointing to the ceiling.

Number 43

From Right Dragon stance turn one hundred and eighty degrees left into Left Dragon stance.

At the same time both arms sweep down and up to finish extended forwards at shoulder height (palms facing down).

Number 44

From Left Dragon stance raise your left leg into Left Crane stance (left knee bent, thigh parallel to the floor) bend your right knee to aid your balance.

At the same time your right arm circles to the right to extend sideways at shoulder height with your right wrist drooped. Your left hand circles to finish covering the front of your right shoulder (not touching).

Number 45

From Left Crane stance step forwards into Left Dragon stance (using the Taoist Walk).

At the same time your left hand circles forwards to finish extended at shoulder height (fingertips pointing to the ceiling, palm facing away from you). Your right arm makes a slight circular movement forward, finishing in the same position as movement forty-four.

Number 46

From Left Dragon stance turn ninety degrees to the right into Left Leopard stance, first take your weight onto your right leg, move your left leg then drift your weight back onto your left leg.

At the same time your left hand circles over to finish palm facing down and your right arm circles under to finish palm facing up (see photograph).

Number 47

From Left Leopard stance turn ninety degrees to the right into Right Dragon stance.

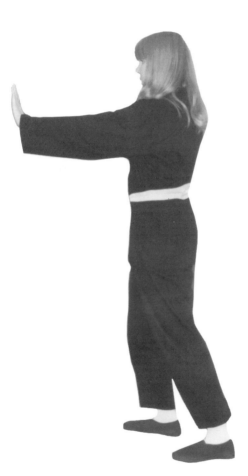

At the same time your right arm circles forwards finishing near your temple with your palm facing to the right. Your left arm circles forwards to finish extended at shoulder height (fingertips pointing to the ceiling, palm facing away from you).

Number 48

From Right Dragon stance step forwards with your left leg into Left Dragon stance (using the Taoist Walk).

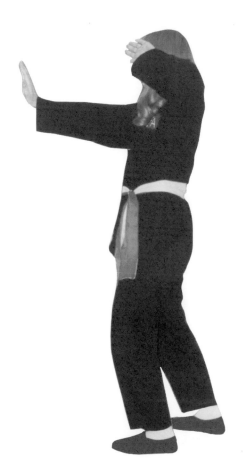

At the same time your right arm extends forwards at shoulder height (palm facing away from you, fingertips pointing to the ceiling). Your left hand moves back to your left temple (palm facing left, fingertips pointing forwards).

Number 49

From Left Dragon stance turn ninety degrees to your right into Left Leopard stance. This is achieved by taking your weight onto your right leg, stepping with your left leg, before correcting your right foot.

At the same time your right arm circles down and over to form the top part of your ball, your left hand circles downwards, turning your left palm up (see photograph for number fifty-three).

Number 50

From Left Leopard stance turn ninety degrees to your right into Right Dragon stance (using the Taoist Walk).

At the same time your right hand circles forwards then back to your right temple to finish with your right palm facing to the right. Your left arm finishes extended forward at shoulder height (palm facing away from you, fingertips pointing to the ceiling).

Number 51

Stay in Right Dragon stance for number fifty one.

At the same time turn your left shoulder to the right. Now fold your left arm in from your left elbow (see photograph).

Number 52

From Right Dragon stance step forward into Left Dragon stance using the Taoist Walk.

At the same time line up the index fingers of both

 hands, with the palms facing away from you (fingertips of left hand pointing to the right and the fingers of the right hand pointing straight up) see photograph.

Number 53

From Left Dragon stance turn ninety degrees to the right into Left Leopard stance, using the Taoist Walk.

At the same time your right hand circles downwards, then upwards and over forming the top of a ball (palm facing down). Your left hand circles downwards forming the bottom of the ball (palm facing up).

Number 54

From Left Leopard stance turn ninety degrees to your right into Right Dragon stance using the Taoist Walk.

At the same time both arms sweep downwards then up to finish extended forwards at shoulder height (palms facing away from you, fingertips pointing to the ceiling).

Number 55

From Right Dragon stance turn one hundred and eighty degrees to your left into Left Dragon stance using the Taoist Walk.

At the same time allow both arms to sweep downwards then upwards, finishing extended forwards at shoulder height (palms facing down).

Number 56

From Left Dragon stance raise your left Leg into Left Crane stance (knee bent, thigh parallel to the floor), bend your right knee to help your balance.

At the same time your right arm sweeps slightly down and up to finish extended sideways at shoulder height (wrist drooped). Your left hand follows your right finishing with your left palm facing your right shoulder.

Number 57

From Left Crane stance step into Left Dragon stance.

At the same time your left arm sweeps forwards to finish extended in front of your left shoulder palm facing away from you, fingertips pointing to the ceiling. Your right hand remains in the same position as it was in for number fifty six.

Number 58

From Left Dragon stance turn ninety degrees to your right, into Eagle stance. This is achieved by taking your weight onto your right leg, pivoting on the heel of your left, then drawing your right foot in.

At the same time your right palm faces your left shoulder and your left arm is by your left side (palm facing up, fingertips pointing forward).

Number 59

From Eagle stance bend both knees into Bee stance.

At the same time both arms sweep forwards in front of the body (palms facing in), right hand level with the shoulder, left hand is in the centre of the body at waist height.

Number 60

From Bee Stance turn ninety degrees to your left into Left Dragon stance.

At the same time your left hand sweeps to the left to finish extended forwards at shoulder height (palm facing away from you, fingertips pointing to the ceiling). Your right arm sweeps to finish extended sideways at shoulder height (wrist drooped).

Number 61

From Left Dragon stance step slightly to the rear with your right foot into Extended Left Duck stance (left leg straight, right leg bent).

Your right hand remains in the same position. Your left hand sweeps to finish in front of your left shin (palm facing down).

Number 62

From Extended Left Duck stance raise your right leg into Right Crane stance (right knee bent, thigh parallel) bend your left knee to aid your balance.

At the same time your right hand circles down then up to finish at the right hand side of your head (palm facing to the left). Your left hand moves down by your left side (palm facing the floor).

Number 63

From Right Crane stance put your right foot down and come up into Left Crane stance.

At the same time your right hand moves down by your right side (palm facing the floor). Your left hand circles up to the left hand side of your head (palm facing to the right, fingertips pointing to the ceiling).

Number 64

From Left Crane stance step behind with your left leg into Right Snake stance (heel down first).

At the same time your left hand extends forwards at shoulder height and your right hand extends behind at shoulder height (both hands palms facing up). Look behind at your right hand.

Number 65

From Right Snake stance transfer your weight back into Right Duck stance (do not move your feet).

At the same time your right arm extends forward at shoulder height (palm facing away from you, fingertips pointing to the ceiling).Your left arm moves by your left side (palm facing the floor).

Number 66

Stay in Right Duck stance for movement sixty-six.

Your right arm remains in the same position, except that your palm now faces downwards. Your left arm sweeps behind and upwards at shoulder height (palm facing up).

Number 67

From Right Duck stance step behind with your right foot into Left Duck stance.

At the same time your right arm swings down by your right side (palm facing down). Your left arm swings up and extends forward at shoulder height (palm facing away from you, fingertips pointing to the ceiling).

Number 68

Stay in Left Duck stance for movement sixty eight. Your left hand turns palm facing up. Your right arm swings up behind you extended at shoulder height, p a l m facing up (looking behind at your right hand).

Number 69

From Left Duck stance step behind with your left foot into Right Duck stance.

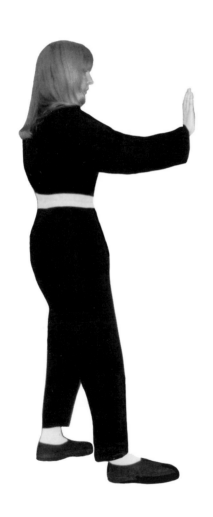

At the same time your right hand swings through to finish extended forwards at shoulder height (palm facing away from you, fingertips pointing to the ceiling). Your left arm swings down by your left side (palm facing the floor).

Number 70

Stay in Right Duck stance for number seventy.

Your right hand moves across your body to finish waist height (palm facing in, fingertips pointing to the left). Your left hand moves upwards and finishes with the left palm facing away from you diagonally, fingertips pointing to the ceiling.

Number 71

From Right Duck stance turn one hundred and thirty five degrees to the right into Right Dragon stance (on the right diagonal).

At the same time your right hand sweep forward and round as the body moves into position, to finish extended at shoulder height (palm facing towards you, fingertips pointing to the left). The left hand moves down by your side palm facing down.

Number 72

From Right Dragon stance move your weight back into Right Monkey stance (left knee bent, right leg straight, toes raised).

At the same time both hands move into the centre of the body (palms facing in, fingertips of the left hand level with the right wrist).

Number 73

From Right Monkey stance turn ninety degrees to the left into Left Leopard stance (left diagonal).

At the same time your left hand moves up level with your forehead (palm facing away from you, fingertips pointing to the right).

Simultaneously your right hand moves palm facing down to finish just below your navel (fingertips pointing to the left).

Number 74

From Left Leopard stance turn one hundred and thirty five degrees to your right into Right Dragon stance.

At the same time your right arm circles forwards and back to finish near your right temple (archer), palm facing away from you. Your left hand extends forwards at shoulder height (palm facing away from you, fingertips pointing to the ceiling).

Number 75

From Right Dragon stance step forward into Left Dragon stance using the Taoist Walk.

At the same your right hand moves forwards to finish at shoulder height (palm facing away from you, fingertips pointing to the ceiling). Your left hand moves back towards the temple (archer), palm facing away from you.

Number 76

From Left Dragon stance, step into Left Cat stance. At the same time both hands circle down, finishing just below the navel (palms facing up, fingertips pointing towards each other).

Number 77

From Left Cat stance, step behind with your left foot into Right Monkey stance (left knee bent, right leg straight, toes raised).

At the same time circle both hands up and round to finish in front of your shoulders (palms facing away from you, fingertips pointing to the ceiling).

Number 78

From Right Monkey stance step forward into Right Dragon stance using the Taoist Walk.

At the same time push forwards with both hands.

Number 79

From Right Dragon stance drift your weight back into Right Duck stance (left knee bent, right leg straight, draw your front foot in a little).

At the same time both hands turn palms in and draw back towards the body, finishing with the fingertips of the left hand level with the wrist of the right hand.

Number 80

From Right Duck stance turn one hundred and eighty degrees to the left into Left Dragon stance.

At the same time both arms fold in to the elbows (see photograph).

Number 81

From Left Dragon stance draw back into Left Cat stance (right knee bent, ball of your left foot resting lightly on the floor).

At the same time your right arm unfolds to extend forwards with your elbow bent (right palm facing up). Your left hand moves to guard just above your right elbow.

Number 82

From Left Cat stance swing your left leg forward into Left Dog stance (bend your right knee to aid your balance).

At the same time pull your right hand back near to your right ear (palm facing to your right). Your left hand extends forwards at shoulder height (palm facing away from you, fingertips pointing to the ceiling).

Number 83

From Left Dog stance swing your left leg directly behind you into Right Chicken stance.

At the same time your left hand remains in the same position as for number eighty two. Your right hand moves by your right side (elbow into the waist, hand in a fist).

Number 84

From Right Chicken stance turn ninety degrees to the left into Left Active Leopard stance (your left leg is bent, your right leg is straight with the heel of your right foot raised).

At the same time both your arms sweep over to the left with the turn of your body. Finish with the fingertips of the left hand pointing up and the fingertips of your right hand pointing to the left (palms facing away from you).

Number 85

From Left Active Leopard stance raise your right leg out sideways into a Right Dog stance (foot pointing to the right), toes pointing upwards.

Your left arm remains in the same position as it was in for number eighty four. Your right arm sweeps out sideways at shoulder height (palm facing away from you, fingertips pointing to the ceiling).

Number 86

From Right Dog stance step through into Right Dragon stance with your right leg (using the Taoist Walk).

At the same time both arms circle down then up to finish in front of the head (both hands form loose fists, facing each other).

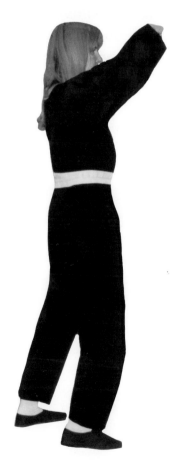

Number 87

From Right Dragon stance step through into Left Cat stance (the ball of your left foot resting lightly on the floor, your right knee is slightly bent).

At the same time both arms circle downwards, your right arm finishes extended forwards with the elbow slightly bent (palm facing up). Your left arm moves across to guard just below your right elbow.

Number 88

From Left Cat stance raise your left leg into Left Dog stance.

At the same time pull your right arm back near to your right ear (palm facing to the right). Your left hand extends forwards at shoulder height (palm facing away from you, fingertips pointing to the ceiling).

Number 89

From Left Dog stance turn ninety degrees to your left into Left Active Leopard stance (the same movement as number eighty four).

At the same time your hands move into the same position as number eighty-four.

Number 90

From Left Active Leopard stance move your right leg out sideways to your right (your toes point to the right). This is classed as a Right Dog stance (see number eighty five).

At the same time circle both arms slightly to your left, then down to finish with your right arm extended sideways at shoulder height. Your left arm finishes near to your right shoulder (see photograph).

Number 91

From Right Dog stance turn your body ninety degrees to the right into Right Flighted Dragon stance (the heel of your left foot is raised).

First, your left hand circles over to the left and down to finish in front of the body (palm facing away from you, fingertips angled on the diagonal). At the same time your right hand moves to form a fist at your right hand side (elbow into the waist).

Number 92

From Right Flighted Dragon stance step forwards into Left Dragon stance (using the Taoist Walk). At the same time both arms extend forwards (bent at the elbows) fingertips angled in towards the centre (palms facing down).

Number 93

From Left Dragon stance raise your left leg into Left Crane stance (knee bent, thigh parallel).

At the same time your right arm sweeps sideways to the right (shoulder height, on the diagonal) the wrist is drooped on your right hand (you are looking at your right hand). Your left hand sweeps across to lay in front of your right shoulder.

Number 94

From Left Crane stance step forwards into Left Dragon stance (using the Taoist Walk).

At the same time your right arm now extends sideways (wrist still drooped). Your left arm sweeps forwards at shoulder height (palm facing away from you, fingertips pointing to the ceiling).

Number 95

From Left Dragon stance turn ninety degrees to the right into Eagle stance (using the Taoist Walk).

At the same time your left arm moves into your left side, palm facing up (fingertips pointing forwards). Your right hand sweeps across to finish in front of your left shoulder.

Number 96

From Eagle stance step sideways into Left Leopard stance (left knee bent, right leg straight).

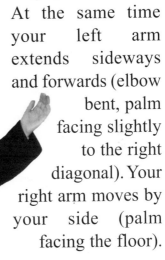

At the same time your left arm extends sideways and forwards (elbow bent, palm facing slightly to the right diagonal). Your right arm moves by your side (palm facing the floor).

Number 97

From Left Leopard stance turn ninety degrees to the right into Right Dragon stance.

Your left arm pushes forwards to finish at shoulder height (palm facing away from you with your fingertips pointing to the ceiling). Your right arm finishes by your right side (palm facing the floor)

Number 98

From Right Dragon stance turn one hundred and eighty degrees into Right Cat stance (pivoting on the heel of your left foot).

At the same time move both hands in front of the body (palms facing each other) fingertips curved in towards each other.

Number 99

From Right Cat stance, swing your right leg forwards into Right Dog stance.

At the same time your right arm extends forwards at shoulder height (palm facing away from you, fingertips pointing to the ceiling). Pull your left hand back near to your left ear (palm facing to the left).

Number 100

From Right Dog stance swing your right leg behind into Left Dragon stance (placing your heel down first).

At the same time both hands move in front of your body (palms facing in) the fingertips of your right hand are level with your left wrist .

Number 101

From Left Dragon stance draw back into Left Cat stance (the ball of your left foot resting lightly on the floor).

At the same time cross both arms in front of your chest (left arm furthest away from you). Your right hand is in front of your left shoulder and your left hand is in front of your right shoulder.

Number 102

From Left Cat stance swing your left leg forwards into Left Dog stance.

At the same time swing both arms forwards and up to finish with your fingertips angled in towards each other (palms facing away from you).

Number 103

From Left Dog stance step forwards into Left Dragon stance (using the Taoist Walk).

At the same time your left arm extends forwards at head height (little finger edge down, palm facing to the right). Your right arm extends sideways at shoulder height (wrist drooped).

Number 104

From Left Dragon stance turn ninety degrees to the right into Frog stance.

At the same time your right arm remains at shoulder height (wrist drooped). Your left arm extends sideways palm facing forwards.

Number 105

From Frog stance come up into Left Leopard stance (left knee bent, right leg straight).

Your left arm remains in the same position, although you raise your left hand slightly. Your right arm folds in at chest height (palm facing down) in front of your body.

Number 106

From Left Leopard stance, swing your right leg out sideways with your toes pointing upwards into Right Dog stance.

Your left arm remains in the same position as number 105.

Your right arm swings out sideways (fingertips pointing to the ceiling).

Number 107

From Right Dog stance turn your body ninety degrees to
your right into Right Dragon stance.

At the same time your
right arm circles over to
the right to finish by
your right side (palm
facing down to the
floor). Your left arm
curves over to finish in
front of your body
(palm angled halfway
between facing away
from you and facing
down).

Number 108

From Right Dragon stance step forwards into Left Dragon stance (using the Taoist Walk).

At the same time your left arm circles over to the left hand side of your body (palm facing down to the floor). Your right arm curves over in front of your body (palm angled halfway between facing down and away from you).

Number 109

From Left Dragon stance step behind with your left foot (placing the heel down first) into Right Monkey stance (left knee bent, right leg straight with the toes raised on your right foot).

At the same time both hands circle to finish palms facing in towards your body (chest height), fingertips opposite each other.

Number 110

From Right Monkey stance turn one hundred and eighty degrees to your left into Left Dragon stance.

At the same time both hands turn over so that they now face away from you (chest height), fingers pointing towards each other.

Number 111

From Left Dragon stance take your weight back onto your right leg into Left Duck stance (right leg bent, left leg straight).

At the same time your left arm is extended forwards at shoulder height (palm facing away from you, fingertips pointing to the ceiling). Your right arm is pulled back with the heel of your hand adjacent to your right hip (palm facing to the left).

Number 112

From Left Duck stance step through into Right Dragon stance (using the Taoist Walk).

At the same time the left hand moves beside the left hand side of the head (salute). Your right hand remains in the same position as it was in for number one hundred and eleven.

Number 113

From Right Dragon stance lift your left leg into Left Stork stance (bending your left knee and taking it behind).

At same time your right hand circles clockwise round the centre of your head (palm facing down). Your left hand remains in the same position as it was in for number one hundred and twelve.

Number 114

From Left Stork stance take your left leg behind your right leg into Left Scissors stance (heel raised on your left foot).

At the same time your left arm extends upwards on the diagonal and your right arm forms a downwards diagonal (pointing with your index finger). Look at your right hand.

Number 115

From Left Scissors stance turn your body ninety degrees to the left into Bear stance (feet shoulder width apart, toes pointing forwards).

At the same time your right arm extends out sideways (shoulder height) palm facing to the right (fingertips pointing to the ceiling). Your left arm moves by your left side (palm facing down towards the floor).

Number 116

From Bear stance raise your left leg with the knee bent into Left Crane stance (foot over the right knee). At the same time both arms extend out sideways at shoulder height (palms facing away from you, fingertips pointing to the ceiling).

Number 117

From Left Crane stance turn ninety degrees to your left into Left Dragon stance (using the Taoist Walk).

At the same time your right hand pushes forwards at shoulder height (palm facing away from you, fingertips pointing to the ceiling). Your left arm moves by your left side (palm facing the floor).

Number 118

From Left Dragon stance, step through into Right Dragon stance (using the Taoist Walk).

At the same time your left arm pushes forwards and up to shoulder height (palm facing away from you, fingertips pointing to the ceiling). Your right arm moves by your right side (palm facing down towards the floor).

Number 119

From Right Dragon stance swing your left leg up into Left Dog stance (bending your right leg slightly to aid your balance).

At the same time your right hand circles forwards then draws back near to your right ear (palm facing to your right). Your left hand remains in the same position as it was in for number one hundred and eighteen.

Number 120

From Left Dog stance step through into Left Dragon stance (using the Taoist Walk).

At the same time your right hand turns palm facing to the left as it forms a fist (thumb on the top). Your right arm is extended forwards at shoulder height. Your left hand moves across to guard your right elbow.

Number 121

Stay in Left Dragon stance for number one hundred and twenty one.

At the same time your left arm forms the top part of a ball shape, at chest height (palm facing down). Your right hand forms the underneath part of the ball (palm facing up), just below the navel.

Number 122

From Left Dragon stance, step through into Right Dragon stance (using the Taoist Walk).

At the same time your left arm circles over and down to the left finishing by your left side (palm facing the floor). Your right arm extends forwards at shoulder height (palm facing in towards you, fingertips pointing to the left).

Number 123

From Right Dragon stance, step through into Left Dragon stance (using the Taoist Walk).

At the same time your right arm circles down by your side (palm facing the floor). Your left hand circles upwards to extend forwards at shoulder height (palm facing in towards your body, fingertips pointing to your right).

Number 124

Stay in Left Dragon stance for number one hundred and twenty four.

At the same time your left arm forms the top of a ball shape, at chest height (palm facing down). Your right hand is underneath forming the bottom of the ball (palm facing up), just below the navel.

Number 125

From Left Dragon stance, step through into Right Dragon stance (using the Taoist Walk).

At the same time both hands push out forwards at shoulder height (palms facing towards you, fingertips pointing to the ceiling).

Number 126

From Right Dragon stance drift your weight back onto your left leg into Right Monkey stance (left leg bent, right leg straight with the toes raised).

At the same time circle both hand out and round to finish in front of your shoulders (palms facing away from you, fingertips pointing to the ceiling).

Number 127

From Right Monkey stance step forwards into Right Dragon stance (using the Taoist Walk).

At the same time push forwards with both hands (palms facing away from you, fingertips pointing to the ceiling).

Number 128

From Right Dragon stance step behind with your left foot into Extended Right Duck stance (placing your heel down first).

At the same time your right arm stays in the same position as it was in for number one hundred and twenty seven. Your left arm sweeps out sideways at shoulder height (wrist drooped).

Number 129

Stay in Extended Right Duck stance for movement one hundred and twenty nine.

Your left hand remains in the same position as it was in for movement one hundred and twenty eight. Your right hand sweeps anti clockwise and finishes in front of your right shin (do not strain).

Number 130

From Extended Right Duck stance, move your left foot forward into Right Snake stance (both knees slightly bent, weight evenly distributed).

At the same time your right hand sweeps up in front of your forehead. Your left hand circles across to the right side of your body (waist height, palm facing down).

Number 131

From Right Snake stance turn one hundred and eighty degrees to the right into Left Crane stance (left leg raised, knee bent, thigh parallel to the floor).

Your hands remain in the same position as they were in for number one hundred and thirty.

Number 132

Stay in Left Crane stance for number one hundred and thirty two.

At the same time your right hand curves downwards to finish angled palm upwards, just inside the left knee. Your left arm moves by your left side (palm facing the floor, fingertips pointing to the left).

Number 133

From Left Crane stance step forwards into Left Dragon stance (using the Taoist Walk).

At the same time your left arm sweeps up and forwards to shoulder height (palm facing away from you, fingertips pointing to the ceiling). Your right arm floats upwards and sideways to finish at shoulder height (with the wrist drooped).

Number 134

From Left Dragon stance drift your weight back into Left Duck stance (right knee bent, left leg straight). At the same time your left arm remains in the same position, except your palm turns to face upwards. Your right arm extends out behind you at shoulder height (palm facing upwards). You are looking behind you at your right hand.

Number 135

From Left Duck stance draw your left foot in to Left Cat stance (right knee slightly bent, ball of your left foot resting lightly on the floor).

At the same time your right hand turns palm down as your arm glides back down to your side. Your left arm folds in to finish in front of your body at waist height by your right side (palm facing down).

Number 136

From Left Cat stance raise your left leg into Left
Crane stance (left leg raised, knee bent, thigh parallel
to the floor).

At the same time
your left arm
unfolds floating
down by your left
side (palm
facing the floor).
Your right arm
circles up in front of
your forehead (palm
facing forwards,
fingertips pointing
to the left).

Number 137

From Left Crane stance, pivot on your heel turning one hundred and eighty degrees to the right staying into Left Crane stance.

Your hands remain in the same position as they were in for number one hundred and thirty six.

Number 138

From Left Crane stance, step through into Left Dragon stance (using the Taoist Walk).

At the same time your right arm pushes forward and down to shoulder height (palm facing away from you, fingertips pointing to the ceiling). Your left hand remains in the same position as it was in for number one hundred and thirty seven.

Number 139

From Left Dragon stance, step through into Right Dragon stance (using the Taoist Walk).

Your right arm remains in the same position as it was in for number one hundred and thirty eight. Your left hand sweep across to guard the right elbow.

Number 140

From Right Dragon stance, step through with your left leg into Left Dragon stance (using the Taoist Walk). At the same time your left arm extends slightly upwards from your left shoulder (palm facing down). Your right arm swings behind and slightly down from your right shoulder (palm facing down), forming a diagonal line between both arms.

Number 141

From Left Dragon stance turn ninety degrees to your right into Left Leopard stance (left knee bent, right leg straight).

At the same time your left arm bends at the elbow to finish at shoulder height (palm facing forwards, fingertips pointing to the ceiling). Your right hand faces forwards with your fingertips pointing to your left hand.

Number 142

From Left Leopard stance, using the Taoist Walk come up into Left Stork (left leg raised, with your foot behind).

At the same time both arms sweep across to the centre of the body to form a T bar (left hand underneath the fingers of your right hand) palms facing forwards on both hands.

Number 143

From Left Stork stance turn ninety degrees to the left into Left Dragon stance (using the Taoist Walk).

At the same time your left arm moves forwards to extend at shoulder height (palm facing forwards, fingertips pointing to the ceiling). Your right arm moves by your right side (palm facing the floor).

Number 144

From Left Dragon stance come up into Right Crane stance (raise your right leg with the knee bent, thigh parallel to the floor).

Your left hand remains in the same position as it was in for number one hundred and forty three. Your right hand turns palm up to finish extended forwards at chest height.

Number 145

From Right Crane stance turn one hundred and eighty degrees to your left into Left Flighted Crane stance (this stance takes place in the air). When you land you will be ready for number one hundred and forty six.

At the same time your right hand circles up and crosses your left hand as you jump and turn into number one hundred and forty six. The movement actually finishes while you are in the air with your hands crossed.

Number 146

From Left Flighted Crane, land in Left Dragon stance.

At the same time your left arm sweeps forward to finish extended at shoulder height (palm facing away from you, fingertips pointing to the ceiling). Your right arm sweeps out sideways to finish at shoulder height (with the wrist drooped).

Number 147

From Left Dragon stance raise your right leg into Right Dog stance.

At the same time your right arm sweeps forwards to finish extended at shoulder height (palm facing away from you, fingertips pointing to the ceiling). Your left hand sweeps across to guard your right elbow.

Number 148

From Right Dog stance step forward with your right leg into Right Dragon stance.

At the same time your right hand moves back near to your right ear, (palm facing to theright). Your left, arm pushes forwards to finish extended at shoulder height (palm facing away from you, fingertips pointing to the ceiling).

Number 149

From Right Dragon stance, raise your right leg into Right Crane stance (right knee bent, thigh parallel to the floor).

At the same time both arms circle outwards, then inwards finishing underneath your right knee (both palms facing up, fingertips pointing towards each other).

Number 150

From Right Crane stance step backwards as you turn ninety degrees to your right into Riding Horse stance.

At the same time both hands circle out, upwards and then inwards, to finish above your head like number sixteen in the Form (palms facing away from you, fingertips pointing towards each other).

Number 151

Stay in Riding Horse stance for number one hundred and fifty one.

Circle both arms outwards and down finishing in front of your Tan Tien (both palms facing up, fingertips pointing towards each other).

Number 152

From Riding Horse stance step forwards into Left Dragon stance (using the Taoist Walk).

At the same time raise your left arm to shoulder height (palm facing away from you, fingertips pointing to the ceiling). Your right arm sweeps sideways and upwards to finish at shoulder height (wrist drooped).

Number 153

From Left Dragon stance drift your weight on to your right leg into Left Monkey stance (right knee bent, left leg straight, toes raised).

At the same time both arms circle in to finish like number five of the Form, except the hands are reversed (fingertips of the right hand are level with the wrist of your left hand).

Number 154

From Left Monkey stance turn ninety degrees to the right into Right Dragon stance (using the Taoist Walk).

At the same time your right arm sweeps forwards and up to finish at shoulder height (palm facing in, fingertips pointing to your left). Your left arm moves by your left side (palm facing the floor).

Number 155

From Right Dragon stance, step through into Left Dragon stance (using the Taoist Walk).

At the same time your left hand pushes forwards to shoulder height (palm facing away from you, fingertips pointing to the ceiling). Your right arm moves by your right side (palm facing the floor).

Number 156

From Left Dragon stance drift the weight back onto your right leg into Left Monkey stance (right knee bent, left leg straight, toes raised).

At the same time both hands turn palms facing in and draw back towards the centre of your body (like number five in the Form, except the hands are reversed).

Number 157

From Left Monkey stance, step behind into Right Monkey stance (placing your heel down first).

At the same time both hands circle outwards, then in (palms facing away from you, fingertips pointing to the ceiling) finishing in front of your shoulders.

Number 158

From Right Monkey stance turn one hundred and thirty five degrees to your left into Left Dragon stance, on the diagonal.

At the same time your left hand glides upwards to finish in front of your forehead (palm facing away from you, fingertips pointing to the right). Your right hand glides down the centre line of your body to finish in front of your Tan Tien (palm facing down).

Number 159

From Left Dragon stance turn one hundred and thirty five degrees to the right into Right Snake stance (both knees slightly bent)

At the same time your right arm moves up to finish at shoulder height forming a T Bar with your right arm forming the top of the T and your left arm forming the stem, (like number sixty-two in the Form).

Number 160

From Right Snake stance move your left foot forward, level with your right foot into Eagle stance (heels together toes pointing slightly outwards).

At the same time both arms sweep out sideways to finish extended at shoulder height (palms facing down).

Number 161

From Eagle stance raise your right leg into Right Dog stance.

At the same time your left hand pushes forwards at shoulder height (palm facing away from you, fingertips pointing to the ceiling). Your right hand pulls back, near to your right ear (palm facing to the right).

Number 162

From Right Dog stance place your right foot down and raise your left leg into Left Dog stance.

At the same time your right arm pushes forwards at shoulder height (palm facing away from you, fingertips pointing to the ceiling). Your left hand pulls back, near to your ear (palm facing to the left).

Number 163

From Left Dog stance take your left foot behind your right leg into Left Scissors stance, turning your right foot forty five degrees to the right (diagonally).

At the same time your right arm moves by your right side (palm facing the floor). Your left arm circles over to finish by your right elbow (palm facing the floor).

Number 164

From Left Scissors stance turn forty five degrees to your left into Right Monkey stance (left knee bent, right leg straight with the toes raised on your right foot).

At the same time both arms lift up from the elbows, then your hands circle so that they finish in front of your shoulders (palms facing away from you, fingertips pointing to the ceiling).

Number 165

From Right Monkey stance step forwards into Right Dragon stance (using your Taoist Walk).

At the same time push forwards with both arms (do not lock your elbows).

Number 166

From Right Dragon stance drift your weight back onto your left leg into Right Monkey stance (left knee bent, right leg straight, toes raised on your right foot).

At the same time both palms turn to face each other, finishing like number five in the Form.

Number 167

From Right Monkey stance turn one hundred and eighty degrees to the left into Left Cat stance (the ball of your left foot rests lightly on the floor).

At the same time both arms move to the left hand side of the body, your left arm is by your left side (palm facing the floor). Your right hand is level with your left elbow (palm facing down).

Number 168

Stay in Left Cat stance for number one hundred and sixty eight.

Your right arm circles over to your right side (palm facing the floor). Your left arm circles over to your right side to finish level with your right elbow (palm facing down).

Number 169

From Left Cat stance place your left heel down and raise the toes of your left foot into Left Monkey stance.

At the same time your right arm circles over the top finishing little finger edge down inside your left knee. Your left hand moves by your left side (palm facing the floor).

Number 170

From Left Monkey stance step forwards into Left
Dragon stance.

At the same time
your right arm
glides up to finish
extended forward at
shoulder height
(palm facing away
from you, fingertips
pointing to the
ceiling). Your left
hand moves across
to guard your right
elbow.

Number 171

Stay in Left Dragon stance for number one hundred and seventy one.

At the same time your right hand pulls back near to your right ear (palm facing to the right). Your left arm glides forwards to finish extended at shoulder height (palm facing away from you, fingertips pointing to the ceiling).

Number 172

From Left Dragon stance turn one hundred and eighty degrees to the right into Right Dragon stance.

At the same time your right hand extends forwards at shoulder height, palm facing towards you, fingertips pointing to the left. Your left arm moves by your left side (palm facing the floor).

Number 173

From Right Dragon stance step forwards into Left Dragon stance (using the Taoist Walk).

At the same time your left arm floats up and is extended forward at shoulder height (palm facing away from you, fingertips pointing to the ceiling). Your right arm moves by your right side (palm facing the floor).

Number 174

From Left Dragon turn ninety degrees to your left stepping with your right leg first, into Right Leopard stance.

At the same time your right arm extends sideways with your elbow slightly bent (palm facing forwards, fingertips pointing to the right). Your left hand moves down to finish in front of the right hand side of your body (waist height, palm facing in).

Number 175

From Right Leopard stance turn ninety degrees to your left into Left Dragon stance

At the same time your right hand pushes forward to finish at shoulder height (palm facing away from you, fingertips pointing to the ceiling). Your left arm drifts down to your left side (palm facing the floor)

Number 176

From Left Dragon stance raise the left leg into Left Dog stance.

At the same time your left arm pushes forwards finishing at shoulder height (palm facing away from you, fingertips pointing to the ceiling). Your right hand pulls back near to your right ear (palm facing to the right).

Number 177

From Left Dog stance lower your left foot into Left Cat stance (the ball of your left foot rests lightly on the floor).

At the same time both hands come together (palms facing, fingertips pointing up, similar to praying).

Number 178

From Left Cat stance put the left heel down and raise your right heel into Right Cat stance.

At the same time (still keeping both hands together) move the fingers so that they are pointing downwards.

Number 179

From Right Cat stance raise your right leg into Right Dog stance.

At the same time your left hand pushes forwards at shoulder height (palm facing away from you, fingertips pointing to the ceiling). Your right hand pulls back, near to your right ear (palm facing to your right).

Number 180

From Right Dog stance turn ninety degrees to your right into Bear stance (feet shoulder width apart).

At the same time both hands move inwards to finish in front of your forehead (palms facing away from you, fingertips pointing towards each other.

Number 181

Stay in Bear stance for number one hundred and eighty one.

Both arms circle outwards and down finishing with the palms facing upwards, in front of your Tan Tien.

Number 182

Stay in Bear stance for number one hundred and eighty two. Lower both arms down to your sides.

Number 183

Stay in Bear stance for number one hundred and eighty three.

Sweep both arms upwards to cross in front of your body (your left arm is furthest away from you) palms in front of your shoulders.

Number 184

From Bear stance draw your left foot into Eagle stance (heels together, toes pointing slightly outwards). At the same time lower both arms to your sides.

The LFA T'ai Chi Dance Set is for everyone, this book acts as a beginners guide. To find the inner depth taught within the movements, you may wish to train with us at one of the ever growing number of LFA classes and day courses, a list of which is available on our Website at www.leefamilyarts.com

I hope you have enjoyed learning our T'ai Chi Dance. May you continue the journey of the Lee Family Arts.

Best Regards
Sheila Dickinson
LFA President

THE LFA T'AI CHI LIBRARY

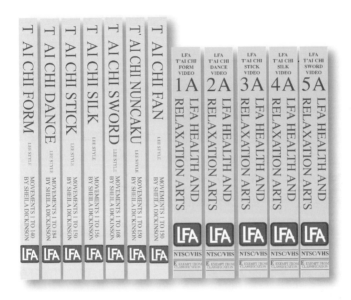

All the above Books and Videos are available from:-

Stairway Distribution Limited
PO Box 19
Hedon
Hull
HU12 8YR
Tel/Fax 01482 896063

You may also order from our Website catalogue, please visit
www.leefamilyarts.com

LFA T'AI CHI DANCE

Notes

LFA T'AI CHI DANCE

Notes

LFA T'AI CHI DANCE

Notes

LFA T'AI CHI DANCE

Notes

LFA T'AI CHI DANCE

Notes